WILLIAM H. ARMSTRONG
author of SOUNDER

Weekly Reader Books presents

THE TALE OF
TAWNY AND
DINGO

illustrated by Charles Mikolaycak

HARPER & ROW, PUBLISHERS
New York   Hagerstown   San Francisco   London

This book is a presentation of
Weekly Reader Books.

Weekly Reader Books offers book clubs for children
from preschool through junior high school.
All quality hardcover books are selected by
a distinguished Weekly Reader Selection Board.

For further information write to:
Weekly Reader Books
1250 Fairwood Ave.
Columbus, Ohio 43216

The Tale of Tawny and Dingo
Text copyright © 1979 by William H. Armstrong
Illustrations copyright © 1979 by Charles Mikolaycak
All rights reserved. No part of this book may be
used or reproduced in any manner whatsoever without
written permission except in the case of brief quotations
embodied in critical articles and reviews. Printed in
the United States of America. For information address
Harper & Row, Publishers, Inc., 10 East 53rd Street,
New York, N.Y. 10022. Published simultaneously in
Canada by Fitzhenry & Whiteside Limited, Toronto.

Library of Congress Cataloging in Publication Data
Armstrong, William Howard, date
The tale of Tawny and Dingo.

SUMMARY: Tawny, the runt sheep of the flock,
discovers a friend in Dingo, the dog, and gains an
unusual kind of courage and leadership.
1. Sheep—Legends and stories.   2. Dogs—Legends
and stories.   [1. Sheep—Fiction.   2. Dogs—Fiction]
I. Mikolaycak, Charles.   II. Title.
PZ10.3.A865Tal 1979   [Fic]   78-19486
ISBN 0-06-020113-4
ISBN 0-06-020114-2 lib. bdg.

To Katie and Chris

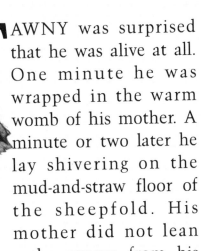

TAWNY was surprised that he was alive at all. One minute he was wrapped in the warm womb of his mother. A minute or two later he lay shivering on the mud-and-straw floor of the sheepfold. His mother did not lean down to clean away the mucus from his mouth and nose, so he was choking. He shook his head, stuck out his tongue, and got one front foot up to rub his nose. At last he felt the air rushing through his nostrils. He was still shivering, but he did not feel so wet and heavy. The air inside him made him feel light. He wanted to get up. He opened his eyes and began to kick his legs back and forth. He wanted to live. He wanted to stand up. He wanted to walk and run.

1

Opening his eyes made him forget his shivering. He rolled his eyes from side to side, up and down, and looked at his new world. Above him and slightly forward stood his mother. Directly under her, and almost stepping on him with their wobbly legs, his brother and sister were drinking milk. His mother turned her head back and forth, licking and smelling the other two as they drank. With every lick the tails of his sister and brother seemed to dance. And with each lick their fleece seemed whiter and softer. Tawny wanted to be licked too. And the sweet smell of his mother's milk came to him. His brother and sister drank so fast they let some spill over their chins. A drop or two splashed on the wet straw near Tawny.

While he was looking and learning, the little lamb moved his legs back and forth. Soon he gathered his hind legs under him and pushed up. They bent, but did not give way.

2

First he got on his knees, then one front leg straightened, then the other. At last he was standing up. Weaving to and fro, he set each foot in turn on the wet straw and mud, proud and happy.

Now Tawny was ready to reach up and find some of that sweet-smelling milk.

But Tawny's mother was confused. She did not welcome that strange-looking lamb. This was surely the ugliest lamb she had ever seen. Mottled brown and white, he looked as though he had wallowed in the mud. His dark-brown spots looked like mud balls stuck in his fleece. One ear and half his face were brown, so that his head looked smaller on one side than on the other.

Now his brother and sister had drunk their fill and Tawny could reach the milk from behind. As the milk warmed him inside, he stopped shivering and wagged his tail. Suddenly a hoof kicked out and sent him sprawling.

He landed where it was wet and slippery. By the time he got to his feet, his mother was far away near the hayrack.

Tawny's feet slipped this way and that on the muddy earth. But the rubbery feeling had gone from his legs. He was just about to try running to catch up with his mother when he found the shepherd and his dog standing in his path. Tawny began to shiver again. He began to bleat for his mother.

"No use," the shepherd said. "You're the wrong number, the wrong color, and the wrong size."

The dog moved in a circle around Tawny, getting closer and closer as Tawny bleated louder and louder. Suddenly the dog stopped and looked down into Tawny's watery eyes. Then he began to lick Tawny's brown ear and the dark side of his face.

"Stop it, Dingo! It's not a pup!"

The dog obeyed his master and stepped

back, but Tawny followed him with his eyes.

"Tawny little runt," said the shepherd. "He'll never make it, Dingo. A triplet is a nuisance. Like I say: wrong number, wrong color, and wrong size."

Dingo did not understand. He would have nuzzled the lamb toward its mother. But the shepherd stood in the way. "A sheep has two nipples for milk. How can she feed three lambs? And she hasn't put her smell on him by licking him clean, so she'll never know him. All that, and only half the size he ought to be. Shouldn't have been born. If he was pure white I could feed him on goat's milk for eight days. Then he could be a sacrificial lamb. But his brown spots make him no good for that. And it'll be a mark on my flock, my beautiful white flock. The other shepherds will laugh."

So the shepherd turned his back on Tawny and tended the pure-white lambs. This was the season for lambs to be born. The shepherd was so busy and happy with the beautiful new lambs that he forgot about Tawny. And Tawny learned quickly to move quietly and to stay away from the shepherd.

He was always hungry at first. But he learned not to bleat like the other lambs. He would move in back of his mother, or even a stranger, and grab a few swallows of milk just when their lambs were finishing. He learned that a mother with one lamb had more milk. Often he could drink quite a bit before he was kicked away.

Tawny was lonely. There were lambs all around, but they ran away or they butted him if he tried to play follow-the-leader. Once or twice Dingo, the shepherd's dog, started to come to his rescue. But the shepherd wouldn't let Dingo chase the lambs.

Tawny liked to be near Dingo. He remembered Dingo's warm tongue licking his ear and face. That was really the only nice thing that had happened to Tawny. But even though he was lonely, and often full of sorrow, Tawny wanted to live.

He marveled at the mysteries around him. Day changed to night and the sheep settled down to sleep. But Dingo sometimes slept during the day, so he moved wide awake and restless at night. Some days a great bright golden ball rose over the sheepfold and the shepherd would stretch forth his arms and exclaim, "Ah! the sun, the sun!" Some days water would drop out of the sky and there would be no sun.

Tawny wondered what lay outside the high walls of the sheepfold. The moon and stars came up over the wall from somewhere out there. Pigeons came over the wall and scratched in the hayseed around the hayrack. They roosted in the top stones of the wall, and their cooing in the gathering dark lulled Tawny to sleep.

There was a space near the wall where no other lambs came because the hay was damp from water seeping under the stones. Here, close to the wall, Tawny could hear footsteps of night prowlers in the darkness beyond. When Dingo made his night rounds, he always turned aside and passed close to where Tawny lay.

When Tawny was old enough to eat barley straw and hay at the hayrack, he was butted and buffeted by the lambs. His own brother was the worst. The sheep squeezed him against the slats and several times he was almost choked.

But Tawny was so small that he could crawl under the hayrack on his knees. Of course, there were only leftovers that the other sheep had dropped, but leftovers were better than bruises.

Even down on his knees Tawny was only half safe. The leader of the flock, the great

ram, strutted around, tossing his head in the air, showing off his curled horns. Tawny stayed as far away as possible.

One day Tawny was nibbling leftovers under the hayrack when he felt a thud and a sharp pain in his side. He found himself high in the air on the great curved horns of the leader. The little lamb was thrown against the stones halfway up the sheepfold wall, dazed but not really injured. His spotted fleece, grown long and curly, cushioned the blow. He landed at the base of the wall. The great bowed head of the ram was coming toward him. Then, out of nowhere, his friend Dingo charged—not to the heels, but straight into the bowed head and horns. Tawny felt the hot breath from the ram's snorting nostrils, and Dingo clamped his teeth on the ram's nose and hung on. He did not let go until the shepherd yelled and waved his crook over Dingo's head. The ram, his nose bloody, shook his head and lowered it, but he walked away.

The frightened pigeons fluttered back to the hayrack. Then Tawny thanked Dingo for saving his life.

After the battering by the ram, Tawny became more cautious. He did not follow the rush of the flock to the feed rack. He waited until the white sheep had eaten their fill and lay about the fold chewing their cuds. Then Tawny went to the feed rack. No one bothered him while he ate choice hay and barley straw instead of chaff crumbs that dropped under the rack. For when the flock had eaten and was not crowding around, the shepherd came and filled the rack from the tall haystacks, so Tawny could pick many a tasty clover.

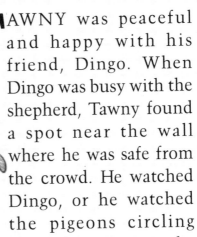

TAWNY was peaceful and happy with his friend, Dingo. When Dingo was busy with the shepherd, Tawny found a spot near the wall where he was safe from the crowd. He watched Dingo, or he watched the pigeons circling against the blue arch of sky. Sometimes he closed his eyes and slept. He liked that, for then he could stay awake with Dingo at night. Sometimes he dreamed that the straw under him was not damp, but that the sun was warming both sides of his fleece at once.

"That mud-colored runt looks like Dingo, the dog." The sheep and lambs said it to hurt, but Tawny didn't mind. Dingo, the sheep dog, was nicknamed Dungo. The lambs hated him. He and Tawny were both brown and white.

Indeed, they were alike under their coats too. Spotted lamb and spotted dog were, in spirit, like brothers. So Tawny did not care at all when the other sheep called him "runt" and "scrub" and "Tawdry."

One day Tawny heard the shepherd say, "The sun is higher now. The moon is full. The time for the sacrifice approaches." The man pointed with his crook and repeated to Dingo, "That one, that one," and so on and on, choosing the largest of the lambs. "Not you, runt," he said as he passed Tawny; "you're the wrong color."

As the sun rose higher in the sky each day, the whole world changed. Days were longer. But Tawny remembered the first grim days and weeks of growing up and these bright days seemed to go too quickly.

Each morning the sheepfold gate was opened and the whole flock followed the leader, his horns held high, out to pasture. The brown earth turned many shades of green, dark and rich in the valleys, bright and golden on the hillsides. The hills stretched on and on until they ran against the sky, blue and shining. Tawny was free. He could feed without being pushed around. And when he had eaten his fill he could lie down by his friend, Dingo.

Now the sheepfold was used only at night to keep the flock safe from wolves and other hungry creatures. The high sun dried the damp straw and mud inside the stone walls. When Tawny lay down near the gate to be close to Dingo, he found a new peace and strength. At first, when the sheep went to pasture, he was pushed against the gateposts and butted off the path. But Dingo said, "Walk with me." So now Tawny waited and walked behind the flock with his dog friend. Deep in his heart he still felt the dull hurt of loneliness, but now new joys filled him.

Tawny loved the warm, life-giving sun. In

the dark hours of night he remembered the sun and hardly felt the chill night wind. Tawny thought of the joy that must come to the pigeons as they circled up and up, higher and higher, closer to the sun.

And at night, when the sheepfold smelled of mildew and stale straw, Tawny remembered the smells of the fragrant earth. He licked his lips and seemed to taste the soft tender leaves he had feasted on during the day. When Tawny slept and dreamed, his dreams were of the green hills and valleys rolling on and on forever. Surely he would never be empty and hungry again.

As Tawny grew, his heart grew. It even had room to hold feeling for the other lambs. "Why are they never still enough to look around and see all the beautiful things?" Tawny asked Dingo.

"Just not thinking," Dingo always said. "Even in the pen at night they are forever

chasing each other, playing leapfrog over their sleepy mothers. And in the pasture they run in gangs, sometimes even into the dark and dangerous edge of the thicket. I can hardly get them back to safety. They will not stand alone to look and listen."

"Not looking," mused Tawny, "they eat the lovely buttercups and windflowers instead of leaving them to brighten the fields. Not listening, they miss the lark's song, so they think nothing of frightening her as they race too near her nest on the grass."

Each morning Tawny followed Dingo out into the summer world. Each day everything seemed fresh and exciting. "Why?" Tawny asked Dingo. "Because what is beautiful is always new," Dingo answered.

Dingo taught Tawny to hear many sounds when they rested together in the shade of a great rock or a thornbush. If Dingo was not busy bringing foolish lambs back from the edge of the thicket, he would lie in the shade with Tawny. At the rustle of a leaf or the snap of a twig, Dingo was up like a flash, ears erect, nose in the air. The harsh, warning call of the raven, the shrill cry of the bush jay, and the chilling silence that followed when the twittering weaverbirds were suddenly still and the lark soared in silence—all these were signs to Dingo. So Tawny learned that danger was never far away. Wolves and bears and other fierce creatures waited in the dark thicket. Watching Dingo, he learned caution and courage.

So listening was important to Tawny. The gentle sounds of earth made him happy to be alive. He heard the breeze skimming the pasture to make the buttercups dance like stars and the windflowers bend and sway. He heard the wind whisper among the high boulders guarding the hill pasture.

When Tawny first went to and from the pasture through the sheepfold gate, he lin-

gered behind to be safe from pushing and butting. As time passed he had another reason to be last through the gate. At evening time, if he lingered behind the noisy bleating, the lark's song came to him, soft as evening shadows. And at evening time the finches sang from the highest branches of the hawthorn trees and the peaks of the yews.

Of all the sounds, none gave Tawny more pleasure than the sound of the pasture brook. At evening time he curled his spotted head against his mottled brown side and listened to the laughter of the brook leaping the stones that tried to block its way. He heard the gentle song of the water as it rolled over smooth pebbles. Last of all, as sleep and dreams ran together, he heard it whisper to the grassy banks that guided it on and on to some far river and some far, far sea.

"I wish the whole flock would stop bleating forever," Tawny said to Dingo one day as they rested quietly in the shade. "The bleating disturbs the music of the earth."

"But mothers must call their lambs and the lambs must answer," Dingo replied. "And lambs must answer when the shepherd calls, and follow him, or he would be very angry. If they didn't answer and follow, I would have more than I could do to keep them together. Some would stray away and be lost. Once, before you were alive, two lambs went too far into the thicket. When the shepherd heard their mothers calling frantically, he sent me to search. I found only two bloody, mangled pelts. The shepherd washed the skins in the brook and made a pair of gloves from them."

The big sheep who was leader of the flock held his head high, tossed his sharp horns, and marched at the head of the column. The loud stamping of his hooves seemed to jar the earth. All the lambs admired him.

But Dingo was Tawny's hero. The more

Tawny grew, the more he admired him. And, as the other sheep imitated their leader, Tawny copied Dingo. Dingo was always loyal to the shepherd and obeyed his commands whether the voice was gentle or harsh. Dingo was always brave in the pasture or the sheepfold. In the day, no wild creature lurking in the dark thicket went unchallenged. And at night a distant howl of hunger or a slinking footfall near the fold made Dingo dash to the gate.

The proud, bossy, great-necked leader of the flock meant no more to Dingo than the smallest lamb. Dingo would nip his heels and make him move where the shepherd signaled by his crook.

As time passed, Tawny began to walk more like a dog than a sheep. He cocked his ears and sniffed the air with his nose up-turned. His voice grew more like Dingo's anxious questioning or his deep-throated command than the *baa-baa* of lambs or the

bleat of the older sheep. And, since Tawny was born little, and remained stunted, he never grew much taller than Dingo. He remained the littlest sheep in the whole flock. His brown-spotted fleece grew long and shaggy, so that seen from a distance or lying close together just inside the sheepfold gate, they were hard to tell from one another.

The shadows of the hills grew longer and longer across the valleys. The time for returning to the sheepfold at evening came earlier and earlier. Dingo, studying the sky one day, said to his friend, "Summer is ending. We wish it to go on forever but it doesn't. Winter comes."

Tawny grew very sad at the thought of being pushed and crowded inside the gray walls, with mud and damp straw instead of the green carpet of the pasture with all its sights and sounds. Now he must go back to finding his time alone at the hayrack. His feeling of aloneness was heavier in the crowded fold. The stares of indifference, and sometimes hate, were close enough to see. Tawny could not run away from them as he could on the bright meadow.

"Why so sad?" Dingo asked when he saw Tawny's head begin to droop.

"The thought of losing summer makes me sad," said Tawny. "I don't like to be penned in the fold. I don't like the cold and the rain—and the days without sun."

"But you'll remember summer. Remembering brings back the sun," said Dingo.

The gray days came and Tawny remembered. Bedded down on the damp straw, he closed his eyes and watched the flowers nodding in the meadow. The song of the lark came to him and shut out the wail of winter wind around the sheepfold. In his dreams Tawny listened to the running laughter of the brook he loved so much.

But as winter grew long, some troubled dreams and waking thoughts came to Tawny. He dreamed that he was running, running, running. He ran past stagnant puddles and bleached stones, where the brook should be, but he could not find the running water again. As the last weeks of winter drew near, when the sun stayed longer again above the sheepfold, Tawny heard the shepherd mention shearing time. Then he began to think about his future. Would he never see the brook and the meadow and the wonderful world outside the sheepfold again?

This year, after shearing, he would be the right age for slaughtering. First the lambs were chosen for the ritual sacrifice, then the flock was culled for the butcher. Last year Tawny had been passed over for the sacrifice because he was too small and he was not milk-white. Then he had cared little whether he lived or died. But it was different now. Tawny did not want to die. He did not want to be cut off from the sights and sounds of the glorious earth, or the friendship of brave Dingo.

Tawny kept his deep and troubled thoughts to himself. He did not want to worry his friend, Dingo. For it was part of Dingo's job to help round up the lambs for slaughtering. But Dingo, too, knew the time and the season. He looked at Tawny and dreaded the day when the shepherd would point his staff and Dingo would obey his orders.

"There, Dingo," the shepherd would say, "the one with the split ear, and that bony-rumped one hiding behind those big ewes. Keep them in the corner. Here, that lame critter that was always getting stuck in the high rocks last summer, and that brown-spotted runt that acts more like a dog than a sheep."

"Obedience is my life," Dingo said to himself as terrible thoughts came to him. This one time he would disobey. But would he?

What good would it do? The shepherd would hook Tawny's neck with his crook and drag him, struggling, with those marked for death. Then, Dingo thought, he would make one mad dash and throw himself against the sheepfold gate, calling to Tawny to flee. But the gate was made wolf strong. It would hold fast.

As winter's days ran one after the other, it was as though the sun had died. The two friends spent the long hours together with long silences between talk. Tawny understood the puzzled pity in Dingo's eyes. They were both thinking of the terrible day that would surely come after shearing time.

The dark days brought rain that felt like ice, sleet that pricked like briar thorns. Winter seemed to grow longer and longer. Yet even though spring was late and shearing time delayed, Tawny waited for spring to come. In spring, the twilight cooing of doves would replace the hunger calls of wild creatures slinking closer and closer in the dark. In spring, the joyous flight of the lark would add light to the sky. In spring, the dark, dark ravens and watching vultures would leave their circling and go to the high crags to nest and feed their young.

The shepherd sat by his fire, and he too longed for spring. "The rain must stop," he said to Dingo. "We must go to the village for provisions. And it's time to drive the flock to pasture to find the first green sprigs of grass."

One evening the shepherd shook the last of the barley from the sack. It made one small barley cake. "I'm still hungry," he said to Dingo, "and the wineskin is empty too. We must go to the village. If we hurry we can be back before the night prowlers come out." He hung the wineskin across Dingo's back and folded the barley sack under one arm. Carefully latching the gate behind him, he set off for the village far below.

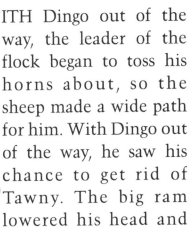

WITH Dingo out of the way, the leader of the flock began to toss his horns about, so the sheep made a wide path for him. With Dingo out of the way, he saw his chance to get rid of Tawny. The big ram lowered his head and charged. The great curved horns buried themselves in Tawny's spotted wool and sent him crashing against the sheepfold gate. Tawny lay still, the breath knocked out of him. Out of the corner of his eye he saw the arched neck and head prepared for another blow.

But suddenly a weasel crept under the gate and sent the flock scurrying and bleating to the far side of the fold. The leader forgot Tawny and began to pace nervously between the weasel and the restless sheep. The weasel made his way to the stone where the shepherd had cooked his barley cake, and dug in the charcoal for a leftover crumb or two. He stood on his hind legs and stared at the milling sheep. Then he passed near Tawny and slipped back under the gate. Tawny regained his breath, but he did not move. Used to lying by the gate with Dingo, he did not join the crowd at the back of the fold.

The haunting cry of a cliff owl sent a new shiver of fear through the flock. They crowded head to tail in a solid mass. The leader paced to and fro. He no longer held his head high; it hung between his forelegs.

Tawny stretched his body a few inches. His side still throbbed with a dull pain. He put his brown-spotted head close to the ground on his outstretched forelegs. From the earth the smell of his friend Dingo came to him. He watched the nervous sheep milling around and around. He listened to them bleating with fear. His eyelids grew heavy, his eyes dimmed. The moving circle grew smaller and smaller. Now it was a patch of windflowers nodding, dancing to a summer breeze. The bleating was gone with the breeze, and Tawny was asleep.

Tawny's dreams of summer were brief. He awakened to the chilling howl of a wolf. At the far side of the fold the flock still stood pressed against each other, frozen with fear. Not a single nervous bleat, not a sound came from the flock except, now and then, the stamping of a hoof, fainter and fainter.

Tawny stood up. A howl shattered the night again, closer now. "Calling for the pack to join him," Tawny thought. "He was probably sitting on his haunches in the high cliff rocks and saw the shepherd and Dingo leave." Tawny had learned well from his friend Dingo.

On the far side of the fold there was a slight stir. The crowd pushed the leader of the flock to the front. The howl came again, so close now it bounced off the walls of the sheepfold and sent an echo back across the night. The leader of the flock turned quickly and squeezed into the crowd.

Tawny moved too. He took four short steps that put him right against the bars of the gate. He peered through the slats.

Many times Dingo had come back from the thicket, calm and unruffled, after driving away danger. And when Tawny remarked how brave he was, Dingo would shrug it off with a wag of his tail. "It's mostly just standing firm with head up," he would say. "Standing firm and a voice without a quiver is all it takes."

Dingo's voice was a deep growl, like two great stones rolling against each other. Tawny wondered if he could growl like Dingo. He had never bleated much. And he always talked to Dingo in a deep whisper so the rest of the flock wouldn't hear and laugh at him.

Tawny looked around the wall of the fold. "The wolf will come to the gate first, sniff, and look around. Then he will circle back, get a running start, and leap the wall. Then comes havoc and death. Me first because I am not in the huddle and I am the littlest sheep in the flock."

Tawny set his ears erect. A loud scraping sound came to him from somewhere in the darkness beyond the gate. "Testing his strength and the sharpness of his claws on a flat stone." Tawny had seen Dingo do it many times when he had sniffed danger near.

The sound of the scraping was very close. Tawny filled his whole insides with deep breaths. His fleece stood out; the deep breaths made him feel taller. He would try to growl like Dingo, then go crowd into the flock and hope.

He had waited too long. Two fiery eyes were staring straight at him through the gate slats. Tawny let all the air in him explode. What a growl! Even loud for Dingo! But letting out the air unbalanced Tawny. He fell as though he were lunging right against the gate. By the time he had righted himself, it came to him—a hollow, halfhearted howl, far away and dying out in the night.

Tawny stood with his nose close against the gate slats, looking out into the dark. He cocked his ears, hoping to hear the shepherd's footsteps coming along the path.

After a short time he could stand no longer; he had to lie down. His body shook, his legs were weakened. His teeth rattled. His body was freezing, but his nose was very hot. He wanted to lick it with his tongue, but he kept his mouth clamped tight. Hearing his teeth rattle made him feel ashamed.

Tawny lay facing the gate, his head on his forelegs. Not once had he turned to look toward the motionless flock squeezed along

the far wall of the sheepfold.

The night was far gone when the shepherd and Dingo returned. Dingo was waddling under a heavy wineskin. His master's shoulders were bent under a load of barley meal and salt. The shepherd peered through the gate, touched the bar to open it, but stopped.

"There's trouble here," he said aloud. "Some varmint killed the runt and is scaring the flock half to death."

The sound of the shepherd's voice roused Tawny from his sleep.

"Must have them cornered," the shepherd said. He pushed back the bar, threw the gate ajar, and rushed toward the hovering flock. As he slipped his burden to the ground, he grabbed a heavy club. "Here, Dingo," he called, and untied the strap that held Dingo's load.

But Dingo did not follow the shepherd

toward the flock. Instead he rushed out growling, his nose sniffing the ground around the fold.

When the shepherd found that no animal was penning his flock against the wall, he came back and stood at the gate for a long time. He glanced down at Tawny, realizing now that he was not dead, then stared into the night. He called Dingo and closed the gate.

"Something happened here," he said, looking again at Tawny, puzzled that he was not cowering like the rest of the flock. "I'll know when morning comes."

This time, strangely, Tawny had felt more hurt at being called "the runt" than ever before. He wondered if the shepherd would ever know what had happened.

Dingo would know. Tawny would tell him in the morning. But for now Tawny moved to the side of his friend, who had stretched his tired body flat before the gate. He heard the shepherd scolding, trying to move the half-smothered flock. They would not move. At last the shepherd gave up trying. Tawny heard him heave a deep sigh as he threw himself down on his sheepskin pallet. That was the last Tawny heard. He edged a little closer to his friend and closed his eyes.

A hard shove in the side by the shepherd's boot wakened Tawny the next morning. "Why do you always have to be in the way?" said the shepherd. "Why aren't you scared and stampeded like the rest? Too dumb, I guess. Come, Dingo!" The shepherd opened the gate and bent over to study the ground. "These aren't your tracks, Dingo," he said suddenly.

Dingo moved to a large slab of stone a little distance from the gate. He smelled, circled the stone, and growled.

"Wolf tracks, that's it," the shepherd said as he moved out toward Dingo, still studying the ground. "Wolf claws! That's it. He was right here for certain."

Dingo stopped sniffing the ground and came to stand by Tawny. He began to lick Tawny's brown-mottled face and wag his tail.

The shepherd watched for a long time and then spoke. "Why, runt, you did it! You look like a dog. You act like a dog. You must even smell like a dog. That varmint thought you were Dingo when he peered through the slats."

The shepherd's excited voice scared Tawny. Besides, the man was coming toward him fast, the way he walked toward some thoughtless sheep who turned aside too far.

Tawny stood still, waiting for a kick in the ribs. But it did not come. The shepherd did something Tawny had never seen him do to anyone except Dingo. He stretched out his leathery hand and patted Tawny on the head. Then he rubbed his fingers back and forth through Tawny's mottled-brown, soft fleece. It made Tawny feel a way he had never felt before. His eyes felt bright and warm like the flame of the shepherd's campfire. The warmth ran down his neck, past his shoulders, through his whole body. When it reached the end of his tail, he felt a strange urge. He wagged his tail!

"Runt," the shepherd said, laughing softly, "you're quite a runt. But you're one runt that will never see the butcher. Anybody can have a sheep dog, but nobody except me has a dog sheep."

When Dingo and Tawny were alone in a quiet corner of the sheepfold, Tawny whispered to his friend all the story of the night before.

"Now you will be the leader of the flock," Dingo said excitedly, when he had heard it all. "They will never follow that coward who huddled in the corner and was as scared as the rest. You will be walking proudly in

front as we go to pasture."

Tawny thought for a long time; then he said, "But you have to walk behind the flock. I would not be walking with you the way we have always gone. No, I will not do it."

"But you would be important," Dingo said.

"No, I won't ever do it." Tawny spoke quietly but firmly.

And so they lay side by side, dreaming of the singing brook and the green pasture.